# THE NEW AVENGERS

## REVOLUTION

Writer: **Brian Michael Bendis**

Art, Issue #26: **Alex Maleev**

Art, Issues #27-31: **Leinil Yu**

Color Art, Issues #27-31: **Dave McCaig**

Letters: **RS & Comicraft's Albert Deschesne**

Assistant Editors: **Molly Lazer & Aubrey Sitterson**

Editor: **Tom Brevoort**

Collection Editor: **Jennifer Grünwald**

Assistant Editors: **Cory Levine & Michael Short**

Associate Editor: **Mark D. Beazley**

Senior Editor, Special Projects: **Jeff Youngquist**

Senior Vice President of Sales: **David Gabriel**

Production: **Jerron Quality Color & Jerry Kalinowski**

Vice President of Creative: **Tom Marvelli**

Editor in Chief: **Joe Quesada**

Publisher: **Dan Buckley**

**PREVIOUSLY:**

It was the worst day in Avengers history. Wanda Maximoff, the Scarlet Witch, suffered a total nervous breakdown after losing control of her reality-altering powers. In the chaos created around the break-down, beloved Avengers Hawkeye, Ant-Man and the Vision lost their lives. Many of the other Avengers were hurt, both emotionally and physically.

Then, the X-Men and the New Avengers found themselves allied against the growing threat of the Scarlet Witch's out-of-control powers. Afterwards, most of the mutants on Earth woke up to find themselves hu-man — without their mutant gene. Only a few hundred mutants remain, when once there were millions. The truth about what happened and the Scarlet Witch's involvement remains a secret to the general popu-lation in order to keep the remaining mutants safe from a growing anti-mutant hysteria.

Those who remember the world that Wanda created refer to it as the "House of M." Clint Barton — Hawk-eye — was reborn in the House of M, and then brutally killed a second time. He reappeared a second time as the world returned to the way it had been. He hasn't been seen since.

NEW AVENGERS VOL. 6: REVOLUTION. Contains material originally published in magazine form as NEW AVENGERS #26-31. First printing 2007. Hardcover ISBN# 0-7851-2445-4. Softcover ISBN# 978-0-7851-2468-9. Published by MARVEL PUBLISHING, INC., a subsidiary of MARVEL ENTERTAINMENT, INC. OFFICE OF PUBLICATION: 417 5th Avenue, New York, NY 10016. Copyright © 2006 and 2007 Marvel Characters, Inc. All rights reserved. Hardcover: $19.99 per copy in the U.S. and $32.00 in Canada (GST #R127032852). Softcover: $14.99 per copy in the U.S. and $24.00 in Canada (GST #R127032852). Canadian Agreement #40668537. All characters featured in this issue and the distinctive names and likenesses thereof, and all related indicia are trademarks of Marvel Characters, Inc. No similarity between any of the names, characters, persons, and/or institutions in this magazine with those of any living or dead person or institution is intended, and any such similarity which may exist is purely coincidental. **Printed in the U.S.A.** ALAN FINE, CEO Marvel Toys & Publishing Divisions and CMO Marvel Entertainment, Inc.; DAVID GABRIEL, Senior VP of Publishing Sales & Circulation; DAVID BOGART, VP of Business Affairs & Editorial Operations; MICHAEL PASCIULLO, VP Merchandising & Communications; JIM BOYLE, VP of Publishing Operations; DAN CARR, Executive Director of Publishing Technology; JUSTIN F. GABRIE, Managing Editor; SUSAN CRESPI, Production Manager; STAN LEE, Chairman Emeritus. For information regarding advertising in Marvel Comics or on Marvel.com, please contact Joe Maimone, Advertising Director, at jmaimone@marvel.com or 212-576-8534.

10 9 8 7 6 5 4 3 2 1

#26

CAN I--?
OH, MY.

IS THE DOCTOR IN?

BY THE HOARY HOSTS...

SORRY TO COME BY WITHOUT AN APPOINTMENT, DOCTOR STRANGE.
DO YOU HAVE A MOMENT?

I READ THE PAPERS BEFORE I CAME HERE.

NO MORE MUTANTS, HUH?

WANDA *REALLY* DID A NUMBER ON EVERYONE.

YES.

AND SHE KILLED ME *TWICE.*

NOT ONCE, TWICE.

YES. BUT... YOU'RE OKAY NOW.

WHERE IS SHE, DOCTOR?

I DON'T KNOW.

HOW COME I THINK YOU DO?

I'M A TRAINED SORCERER, AND YES, I CAN TRACK THE MAGICS ALL OVER THE WORLD AND FIND THOSE WHO ARE USING OR ABUSING THEM.

AND, IN THE PAST, TO FIND *HER,* I HAVE.

ALL I KNOW NOW IS SHE'S NOT USING THEM ANYMORE, SO I CANNOT FIND HER.

THIS CHAOS MAGIC OF HERS, HER MUTANT POWER--

--NONE OF IT IS OUT THERE NOW.

SHE'S DISAPPEARED.

OR NO LONGER WITH US.

KILLED HERSELF?

IT WAS A VERY... *"SHAKESPEAREAN"* ARC SHE TRAVELED.

SHE *MAY* HAVE.

SHE'S NOT THAT KIND OF GIRL.

AND YES, I DID FEEL STUPID JUST SAYING THAT BECAUSE CLEARLY I HAVE NO IDEA WHAT KIND OF GIRL SHE REALLY IS.

MAY I CALL THE AVENGERS NOW?

THEY'D BE SO RELIEVED TO SEE YOU.

NOT YET.

CLOSURE.

I DON'T THINK YOU'LL HAVE IT. *IF* YOU FIND HER, IF BY SOME MIRACLE-- --I DOUBT THAT WHAT YOU'LL FIND WILL HELP YOU FEEL BETTER ABOUT WHAT'S HAPPENED.

BUT REVENGE? REVENGE IS ANOTHER THING ENTIRELY.

I JUST NEED TO KNOW WHY...

IT MAY MAKE THINGS WORSE. YOU MAY--

WHERE WILL YOU LOOK?

WELL, I'LL HEAD OVER TO GENOSHA.

BEING AS THAT'S THE LAST PLACE I SAW HER.

IF SHE'S NOT THERE, AND SHE PROBABLY ISN'T...

NUH!

OH GOOD, YOU'RE AWAKE.

UM...

IT'S THE MOUNTAIN AIR.

YOU HAVE TO GET USED TO IT, I'M TOLD.

WHERE AM I?

IN MY HOME.

THE TOWN DOCTOR IS OUT OF TOWN, WHICH DOES *YOU* NO GOOD, SO WE BROUGHT YOU HERE.

TRY TO KEEP YOUR VOICE DOWN THOUGH, MY AUNT AGATHA IS ASLEEP.

ARE YOU AMERICAN?

AND WHAT ARE YOU DOING ALL THE WAY UP HERE?

YES.

LOOKING...

...FOR A FRIEND.

WHAT'S THEIR NAME? MAYBE I KNOW THEM.

WHAT'S *YOUR* NAME?

WANDA MAXIMOFF.

CLINT BARTON.

I MADE YOU SOME FOOD.

UH... THANK YOU.

AND THANK *YOU* FOR BEFORE. THOSE KIDS...

I'M A WOMAN WITHOUT A MAN. IT MAKES ME A TARGET.

HOW--HOW LONG HAVE YOU BEEN HERE?

MY WHOLE LIFE. MY FAMILY IS GONE, EXCEPT MY AUNT.

PRETTY REMOTE.

WE HAVE INTERNET AT THE POST OFFICE.

SO YOU-- YOU SEE WHAT'S GOING ON IN THE WORLD?

WITH WHAT?

THE MUTANTS.

I TEND TO NOT BELIEVE MUCH OF WHAT I READ IN THE SO-CALLED MEDIA.

I WAIT TEN YEARS AND READ THE BOOK THEY WRITE ON WHAT *REALLY* HAPPENED, BUT WERE TOO AFRAID TO TELL US AT THE TIME.

DID YOU HEAR WHAT HAPPENED...TO THE AVENGERS?

NO.

DO YOU KNOW WHO THEY ARE?

#27

**Ronin**

**From:** "Maya Lopez"
**To:** "Matt Murdock"
**Subject:** Ronin
Hello, Matt. This is Maya Lopez.

I know it's a surprise to hear from me like this...

...especially with what's gone on in the world and in your life.

And how things were left between us...

But if you're reading this, I'm probably dead.

The Tokyo nightlife is filled with two things.

Gangsters blowing off steam on a drug and alcohol fueled nightlife binge--

--that they think actually fills the hole in their soul created by days of dishonor and betrayal--

--and rich, vacant heiresses--the baby rich--who pride themselves on serving absolutely no purpose in the world.

I realized that the best disguise, the best double life, the only one I could think of that was even more ingenious than yours...

...would be vacant, anonymous party girl by night...

...Ronin by late night.

No one looks at the girls. They're just objects.

I could just sit there, like a piece of giggling furniture, and eavesdrop and upload every single piece of information these weak-willed, bragging, spineless Yakuza wannabe #$%^s say...

...and when it's time...

...use it.

Not as Echo, not as Maya Lopez, but as someone they don't know, someone they couldn't trace back.

As a man.

As a figure of the shadows.

As you.

BAM

CRACK

And when the idiots talk of Ronin, they wonder if it's someone new or maybe it's one of the American heroes who has run away from the Civil War.

They wonder: maybe he's Daredevil, maybe he's Iron Fist, maybe he's Nick Fury.

And I love it!

But the point of all of this was to report back to the Avengers.

To work **with** the Avengers on taking this all down from the top as soon as I had a clear picture of what was going on in the upper echelons of the underworld in this part of the world.

But all that went to hell because all of your friends started beating each other up.

The world watched in amazement as America's heroes ripped themselves to shreds.

I watched in horror.

Who were my friends now? Who do I go to when I'm ready?

Captain America recruited me, but Iron Man offered to stake me.

Who do I go to? What side am I on?

Essentially, I found myself stuck out here.

They left me.

I've ripped through their organization so fiercely as Ronin.

I've killed as many of them as I could.

CLANG

It's the only language they respect and understand.

SPACK

But you know as well as I, they don't take it kindly or lightly.

CRACK

They start to **hunt** their prey.

FUGN

And they come after them with an army mentality.

SPAK

An army of assassins.

CHUNK

SPACK

I've never fought Elektra.

As much as I pray for a warrior's death...

...I hope it wasn't her who took me down.

I hope I honored my family. And I hope I honored you.

CRASH

AGH!

I so hope it wasn't her.

HYAAH!

CLANG

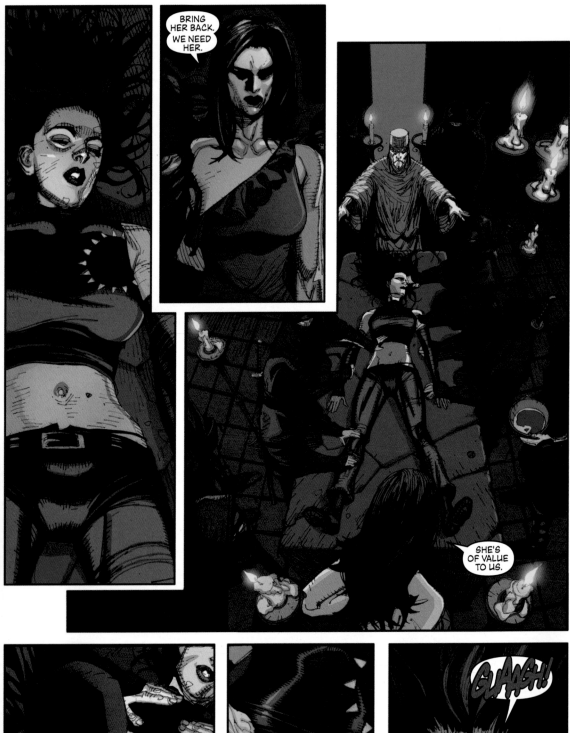

BRING HER BACK. WE NEED HER.

SHE'S OF VALUE TO US.

GUAGH!

MAYA, I KNOW YOU CAN'T HEAR ME, BUT I WANT YOU TO LOOK AT ME AND SEE ME SAY THIS TO YOU.

IT WAS AN HONOR TO FIGHT YOU.

IT WILL BE AN HONOR TO FIGHT ALONGSIDE YOU...

...ONCE YOU'RE READY.

NUH!

AAAGH!

FLUMP

AS YOU KNOW, MAYA...

...THE WAYS OF THE HAND DATE BACK HUNDREDS OF YEARS.

A CODE OF HONOR AND WARRIOR WAYS THAT HAVE SURVIVED THROUGH ALL OF THIS WORLD'S STRUGGLES.

AND YOU ARE A GREAT WARRIOR WITH NO FOCUS OR PURPOSE.

OUR WAYS WILL DEFINE YOU AND THE NEXT PHASE OF YOUR LIFE.

YOU'LL BE PART OF SOMETHING TRULY... PROFOUND.

...it'll only make it worse.

Don't let them crush me!

I mean it, Matt. I'm begging you.

If you can't do it, send someone who can.

Send someone who could break down their walls and fight through them.

Don't let Ronin disappear.

Don't let them turn me into something I despise.

IF THE SCROLLS SAY THREE DAYS THEN THREE DAYS SHOULD BE--

And if they've killed me...

...avenge me.

FOOM

OOF!

THAT *HAD* TO HURT!

DON'T SCREW AROUND! WE GOTTA KEEP MOVING.

DO LIKE WE SAID.

OKAY, OKAY. JEEZ...

HI. MY NAME IS LUKE SKYWALKER AND I'M HERE TO RESCUE YOU.

(SORRY, I ALWAYS WANTED TO SAY THAT.)

COME ON, ALL THE COOL AVENGERS ARE HERE. CAN YOU READ MY LIPS? MATT MURDOCK SENT US TO GET YOU AND WE GOT YOU, SO LET'S...

THE AVENGERSSS BROKE UP.

I KNOW...

THISSS IS A TRICK...

WE'RE THE *NEW* NEW AVENGERS.

COME ON...

NOOO...

I PROMISE I'M HERE TO HELP YOU.

(MAN, WHAT DID THEY DO TO YOU?)

YOU KNOW WHAT YOU NEED? A CHICK FIL-A NUGGETS COMBO MEAL.

WE'LL GET YOU BACK TO THE STATES AND THAT'S THE FIRST THING WE'LL GET YOU...

GOT HER!

THEN LET'S GO!

BUT WE JUST GOT HERE!

DOCTOR, Y'READY?

COME TO ME, AVENGERS.

DANNY!

I'M ON IT.

MATT?

NOT EXACTLY.

WHO *ARE* YOU?

#28

TOKYO, NOW

YIKES-A HOOTY! *THAT* WAS THE TEXTBOOK DEFINITION OF CLOSE!

IT AIN'T OVER YET, SPIDEY.

YOU, LOGAN, AND JESS TAKE A ROOFTOP AND DO THAT THING WHERE YOU KEEP A LOOKOUT.

RECON.

RECON.

YAY! I LOVE ROOFTOP RECON.

KEEP AN EYE AND NOSE OUT FOR THE NINJAS.

MAYA? MAYA LOPEZ, CAN YOU HEAR ME?!

I'M DOCTOR STRANGE! I'M A FRIEND OF MATT MURDOCK'S!

MMMMMATT?

MAYA, CAN YOU TELL ME WHAT THEY DID TO YOU? DID THEY *GIVE* YOU SOMETHING??

SHE CAN'T HEAR YOU. SHE'S DEAF.

TTTHEY KILLED ME... AND THEN BROUGHT ME... TTTHEY BROUGHT ME BACK. AND THEN A BLUE DEMON.

BLUE...

BLUE PILL...

BLUE PILL?

GOOD LORD, THEY WERE TRYING TO BRAINWASH HER.

REAL OLD-SCHOOL NINJA %^&#.

IS IT TOO LATE?

NO. BUT WE HAVE TO GET HER SOMEWHERE SAFE.

WHERE CAN WE GO?

HOSPITAL?

NO. IF THE HAND FOLLOWS US--

--THEY'LL CARVE THROUGH THAT WHOLE PLACE TO GET TO HER. PATIENTS, DOCTORS, NURSES...

THEY'D DO THAT?

YUP.

I KNOW WHERE WE CAN GO.

YASHIDA CLAN FORTRESS
OSAKA, JAPAN

THAT IS SO *FETCH.*

GRETCHEN, STOP TRYING TO MAKE *"FETCH"* HAPPEN.

IT'S NOT GOING TO HAPPEN.

WOULDN'T'A GUESSED THE SILVER SAMURAI TO BE A LINDSEY LOHAN FAN.

WELL, FREAKY FRIDAY *IS* UNDERRATED.

HARADA.

HARADA, YOU *OWE* ME.

ARE YOU PEOPLE OUT OF YOUR MIND? NO.

YOU COME INTO MY HOME, LOGAN? MY *FATHER'S* HOME? AFTER WHAT YOU DID TO ME?

YOU STABBED *ME* IN THE CHEST AND SLICED MY HEART IN HALF.

UH, YIKES.

YOU HAVE MUTANT HEALING POWERS. YOUR HEART GREW BACK.

WE'LL GO. WE DIDN'T KNOW YOU TWO HAD A THING.

YOU TRIED TO KILL *ME*, HARADA.

YOU LOST.

TRY IT AGAIN AND YOU'LL LOSE THE OTHER HAND.

*WHY* ARE YOU IN MY HOUSE?

INFORM DIRECTOR STARK, WE ARE IN AERIAL PURSUIT, OVER.

LUKE CAGE DOESN'T FLY.

HE DOES *NOW.*

I WOULDN'T COME BACK WITHOUT HIM.

OH, MAN.

OH MY GOD.

I'M A'IGHT, JESS.

MISTER CAGE, PLEASE LET WONG DO YOUR SHOPPING. IT'S NOT WORTH THE RISK.

JUST TRYING TO PROVIDE FOR MY FAMILY. JUST TRYING TO STAY SANE.

DOC, ARE YOU SURE NO ONE CAN SEE US HERE?

NO ONE FROM *THIS* DIMENSION, MISS JONES.

I'D EXPLAIN TO YOU THE INCANTATIONS AND SPELL-CONJURING INVOLVED IN MAKING IT APPEAR TO THE WORLD AS THOUGH DOCTOR STRANGE HAS SOLD HIS HOME TO A LARGE, FACELESS CORPORATION WHICH IS DETERMINED TO TURN EVERY INCH OF THIS CITY INTO THE LARGEST STRIP MALL EVER MADE AND MOVED TO EUROPE...

...BUT IT WOULD *BORE* YOU.

I THINK IT ALREADY HAS.

LET'S LEAVE THEM ALONE. THEY'RE DOING THEIR MEDITATION.

DON'T BE SNOOTY, WONG.

FROM NOW ON, WONG'S DOING THE SHOPPING.

GIRL, I'M GOING TO GO SHOPPING WHEN I WANT TO GO SHOPPING.

YEAH, IT'S CUTE THAT YOU THINK SO.

YOU BETTER LISTEN TO THE WOMAN...

I'M SO GLAD TO SEE YOU GUYS. IT'S *ROUGH* OUT THERE.

IS THIS EVERY-BODY?

GUESS SO.

OKAY. I HAVE SOME NEWS.

CAPTAIN AMERICA ISN'T DEAD.

HE'S ALIVE.

THEY GOT HIM ON ICE. THEY'RE HOLDING HIM.

BULL.

WHO TOLD YOU?

CAROL DANVERS.

SHE'S-- SHE'S *LYING* TO YOU.

I DON'T THINK SHE IS. WE HAVE A HISTORY.

WE *ALL* HAVE HISTORIES.

WE ALL HAD DIFFERENT KINDS OF RELATIONSHIPS *BEFORE* THE WAR.

BUT EVERYTHING'S DIFFERENT NOW.

I KNOW.

YOU'RE AN ENEMY OF THE STATE.

NO.

NO?

THEY WANT ME TO COME BACK IN.

THEY DECIDED I'M OF VALUE AGAIN.

I DON'T KNOW, JESS.

SHE DIDN'T SAY IT THE WAY SOMEONE WOULD SAY IT IF THEY WERE LYING. SHE LET IT SLIP.

THAT'S *EXACTLY* HOW A PERSON WHO IS LYING TO YOU WOULD SAY SOMETHING LIKE *THAT.*

I'M A TRAINED AGENT OF S.H.I.E.L.D. AND HYDRA. I KNOW WHEN SOMEONE IS LYING TO--

WHERE IS HE THEN? WHERE ARE THEY KEEPING HIM?

THE RAFT.

THE PRISON ISLAND THING?

WHERE WE FIRST ALL GOT TOGETHER.

THEY WERE USING IT AS A RECON POST DURING THE WAR. NOW IT'S WHERE THEY'RE KEEPING HIM.

IT'S A TRAP.

I'VE BEEN SITTING WITH THIS FOR TWO DAYS AS I MADE MY WAY HERE...

AND ALL I CAN THINK IS, WHAT DIFFERENCE DOES IT MAKE?

IF THE ROLES WERE REVERSED, CAP WOULD DIVE IN TO SAVE US, HEADFIRST.

TRAP OR NO TRAP, HE WOULD GO *GET US.*

YOU'RE RIGHT.

WELL, WE CAN FIND OUT IF IT'S A TRAP, NO PROBLEM.

HOW?

CALL THEM UP AND ASK THEM?

RYKER'S ISLAND MAXIMUM SECURITY PENITENTIARY.

THE RAFT, RYKER'S MAXIMUM-MAXIMUM SECURITY INSTALLATION.

LET ME SEE HIM.

SLIICCCEEEE

HUUAARGGH!

OPEN THE
DOOR.

PLEASE.

OH MY
GOD.

GRAB
HIM AND
LET'S
GO.

WAIT.

≥SNIFF≤

AIN'T
HIM.

SORRY
ABOUT
THAT.

IT WAS A DIRTY TRICK.

BUT YOU'VE CREATED THIS SITUATION. YOU'VE BROUGHT IT DOWN TO THIS LEVEL.

NOT US.

YOU'RE UNDER ARREST.

"WHAT'S WRONG WITH HER?"

NYYAGGHH!

SERIOUSLY, WHY IS SHE DOING THIS?

SHE'S DESPERATELY FIGHTING OFF THE EFFECTS OF THE DRUGS THEY GAVE HER.

SHE'S HAVING INTENSE HALLUCINATIONS. HOLD HER SO SHE DOESN'T HURT HERSELF.

WHAT ARE YOU DOING TO HER NOW?

TRYING TO STABILIZE HER VITAL SIGNS THROUGH A SERIES OF HOMEOPATHIC ENCHANTMENT SPELLS.

WHAT'S HAPPENED TO HER?

THE HAND GOT HER.

AND YOU BROUGHT HER *HERE*?

FIGURED WITH OUR RECENT HISTORY, IT'S CLOSE TO THE *LAST* PLACE THEY'D LOOK.

THEY'LL COME HERE.

ANYWHERE WE GO, THEY'LL FOLLOW.

*I'M* HERE.

LESS CIVILIANS HERE.

WHO ARE THE HAND WORKING FOR NOW?

I'M THINKING WE'LL CHARGE *THEM* AND CUT IT OFF AT THE HEAD.

THE HAND? WHO IS THE *HAND* WORKING FOR? SINCE ELEKTRA NATCHIOS TOOK OVER-- NO ONE.

WHILE YOU WERE OFF HAVING YOUR CIVIL WAR, ALL HELL BROKE LOOSE HERE.

THE WORD WENT OUT JUST TWO WEEKS AGO. EVERYONE IN THE YAKUZA SYNDICATES IS WORKING FOR *THEM*.

AND IF YOU REFUSE... YOU LOSE A *HEAD*.

THE FATHERS ARE FROZEN IN FEAR.

SANTAHORI WAS FOUND IN HIS BED...*WITHOUT* HIS HEAD.

AND THIS ISN'T JUST JAPAN...

AND WHAT ARE YOU *DOING* ABOUT IT? SITTING HERE WATCHING TV?!

I'M PROTECTING MY ANCESTRAL HOME.

≥SNIFF≤ HEY, GUYS?

#29

NNAAGGHH!

CRASH

CRASH

CRASH

CRASH

CRASH

CRASH

CRASH

CRASH

THUMP

YESTERDAY. THE RAFT. MAXIMUM SECURITY PRISON FACILITY OFF THE COAST OF MANHATTAN.

YOU'RE ALL UNDER ARREST FOR VIOLATING THE SUPERHUMAN REGISTRATION ACT.

THE WAR IS OVER, THE LAW IS THE LAW.

THIS WAS DIRTY POOL, MAN.

I MEAN... WOW.

I THINK WE MADE IT PRETTY CLEAR, TONY...

THE WAR IS OVER WHEN WE SAY IT'S OVER.

"NO, WE WERE NOT."

ANOTHER NEIGHBORHOOD STARBUCKS COMING SOON!

ABOUT A MONTH AFTER THE MARCH, ON MAY 15, 1982...

ANDY APPEARED ON SATURDAY NIGHT LIVE, HUMBLED, HIS DAMAGED NECK BUTTRESSED BY A SIZABLE BRACE...

HOLY--!

YOU OKAY?

M'OKAY.

WHAT HAPPENED?

WASN'T CAP?

NOPE.

WHAT DO WE DO NOW?

WELL, WHY DON'T WE--

NUTS.

UH-OH.

DID YOU REALLY HEAR A GUNSHOT?

NO.

THEY CAN'T SEE OR HEAR US. PUT THE CLAWS AWAY, LOGAN.

HE REALLY LEFT HIS HOUSE.

ARE YOU SURE, DOC? STARK'S GOT SOME FANCY TOYS.

THIS IS *SO* WEIRD.

HE'S LIVED HERE FOR AS LONG AS I CAN REMEMBER.

YOU THINK IT'S A TRICK? COULD BE A TRICK.

ARMOR, FULL ENVIRONMENT SCAN.

SCANNING.

SCAN COMPLETE.

ALL ENVIRONMENT LEVELS IN APPROPRIATE RANGE.

SO...?

LET'S GO.

I THINK WE SHOULD MOVE TO THE MOON.

BUT IF ANY OF YOU NEED SOMEWHERE TO SLEEP, MY HOME IS YOURS.

WHEW!

SO, WHAT'S FOR DINNER?

YOU KNOW WHAT? I THINK WE SHOULD SPLIT UP AND REGROUP TOMORROW.

MR. RAND, UM, THE-THE AVENGERS ARE HERE TO SEE YOU?

CAN I HELP YOU?

WE'D LIKE TO TALK TO YOU ABOUT LAST NIGHT.

WHAT HAPPENED LAST NIGHT?

OH, IT'S GOING TO BE ONE OF *THOSE* CONVERSATIONS WHERE ONE OF US PRETENDS TO NOT KNOW WHAT THE OTHER ONE IS GOING TO SAY.

OKAY... LAST NIGHT, YOU, AS IRON FIST, WERE AMONG A GROUP OF VIGILANTES THAT BROKE INTO A S.H.I.E.L.D. FACILITY.

ARE YOU SURE YOU WANT TO HAVE THIS CONVERSATION IN FRONT OF YOUR STAFF?

LAST NIGHT I WAS HERE.

YOU CAN CHECK THE COMPUTER LOGS WITH YOUR FANCY COMPUTER SUIT.

PLEASE SPARE ME THE--

WASN'T ME.

MIGHT HAVE BEEN ONE OF THOSE COPYCAT COSTUME GUYS.

WEREN'T THERE LIKE *THREE* DAREDEVILS RUNNING AROUND A LITTLE WHILE AGO?

DANNY, YOU'RE BREAKING THE LAW AND NOW ALL THE GOOD YOU'VE DONE IN THE WORLD IS--

I'M JERYN HOGARTH, MISTER RAND'S ATTORNEY...*WHAT* LAW IS HE BREAKING EXACTLY?

AND *SPEAK UP.* WE'RE DIGITALLY RECORDING THIS MEETING.

I KNOW.

FIRST OF ALL, HE IS NOT REGISTERED WITH S.H.I.E.L.D.

OF *COURSE* YOU'RE RECORDING THIS.

BUT I *AM* REGISTERED--

EXCUSE ME, DANNY--BUT MY CLIENT *IS* REGISTERED WITH THE UNITED STATES AS A LETHAL WEAPON AS IS THE LAW.

YOU *ALSO* HAVE TO REGISTER YOURSELF AS A--

*THAT* HAS YET TO BE LAID OUT IN A COURT OF LAW.

WE HAVE AN APPEAL IN WITH THE FEDERAL COURT SYSTEM TO DEFINE EXACTLY WHAT IS A POWER--

THEN I HOPE YOU'RE PREPARED TO HAVE *ALL* THOSE FILES AND THAT TECHNOLOGY *SUBPOENAED* BY THE HIGHEST COURTS IN THIS COUNTRY.

BE STILL, YOU WIG-WEARING HUMP.

DANNY, PLEASE, TELL LUKE AND JESSICA THAT THEY HAVE A *BABY* AND THAT THIS IS A *VERY* DANGEROUS GAME YOU'RE PLAYING.

WHAT ON *EARTH* IS THE *GOAL* FOR YOU GUYS?

WHAT DO YOU THINK YOU'RE GOING TO *GAIN* FROM THIS? SOMEONE IS GOING TO GET HURT.

YOU MEAN SOMEONE *OTHER* THAN CAPTAIN AMERICA?

ARE YOU PRESSING CHARGES AGAINST MY CLIENT, AND IF SO, WITH WHAT PHYSICAL EVIDENCE?

COUNSELOR, UNDERSTAND HOW THE TECHNOLOGY OF MY ARMOR WORKS.

I HAVE SCANS, RADARS AND ENVIRONMENTAL SENSORS RUNNING AT ALL TIMES AND RECORDING EVERY AND ANYTHING I COME IN CONTACT WITH, INCLUDING LAST NIGHT--

IF YOU ADMIT ONE FILE, WE'LL SUBPOENA *ALL* THE FILES.

WHICH DO YOU THINK WILL LAST LONGER, THE TRIAL OR YOUR TENURE AS DIRECTOR OF S.H.I.E.L.D.?

MAYBE WE SHOULD GO BACK AND FIGHT BROTHER VOODOO.

STOP!

WE'RE NOT HERE TO FIGHT YOU, ELEKTRA!

'CAUSE AT *THIS* POINT WE'RE ON THE SAME SIDE!

YOU HURT ONE OF OURS. WE CAME TO GET HER.

*THAT'S* BUSINESS.

KTANG

BUT THE FACT OF THE MATTER IS YOU CAN THROW ALL THE SWORDS YOU GOT AT ME, YOU AIN'T GONNA PUT A DENT IN ME.

AND LOGAN'S BEEN SPLIT IN TWO BY MORE THAN ONE OF YOU, AND HE'S *STILL* HERE.

AND WHILE ALL'A THAT'S GOIN' ON, DOC STRANGE CAN WHIP SOMETHING UP--TURN YOU INTO A BUNNY.

YOU *AIN'T* GONNA WIN THIS FIGHT, ELEKTRA.

NOT THE BEST WAY TO START YOUR REIGN AS QUEEN OF THE JAPANESE UNDERWORLD.

BUT ON THE OTHER HAND, NO PUN INTENDED... YOU *NEED* US.

WE'RE CRIMINALS NOW, THAT'S THE HAND GOD DEALT.

YOU READ THE PAPER--THAT'S HOW IT IS NOW.

SO, CRIMINAL TO CRIMINAL...

LET'S TALK.

#30

NEW YORK CITY, EARLIER TODAY.

S.H.I.E.L.D. COMMAND TO DIRECTOR STARK.

NO UPDATE. HOLD STEADY, HELICARRIER. BROTHER VOODOO IS IN THERE DOING--

THAT VOODOO THAT *HE* DO.

CAROL.

OH, LIKE YOU WEREN'T *DYING* TO SAY IT.

*THIS IS SERIOUS.*

I KNOW.

DOCTOR STRANGE IS IN HIS HOME AND HE IS *HIDING* FROM US.

MAYBE. HE IS.

TELL ME WHEN.

HOLD STILL, ARES.

I HATE THIS MAGIC $%#@.

THANK YOU.

*YOU* KNOW WHAT I MEAN.

IT'S THE ONLY THING KEEPING US OUT OF *JAIL*, WOLVERINE.

I MEANT THE VOODOO GUY. *HIS* MAGIC I DON'T LIKE.

DOC, IF WE GOT TO THROW DOWN, WE'LL THROW DOWN...

NOT WITH MY KID IN THE ROOM.

YEAH, UH, NO $%^#.

HOLD ON...

A DOLLAR FOR WHOEVER TELLS ME WHAT'S GOING ON.

I SWEAR, A WHOLE DOLLAR.

WAIT...

WELL..?

DOCTOR STRANGE IS NOT IN THERE. NO ONE IS IN THERE.

YOU'RE SURE?

NO.

NO?

NO.

ANOTHER NEIGHBOR STARBUCKS COMING

HE'S CALLED THE *MASTER* OF THE MYSTIC ARTS FOR A REASON.

HE *IS* THE MASTER.

HE KNOWS MORE ABOUT WHAT HE KNOWS THAN ANYONE ON THE PLANET.

SO THERE *MAY* BE A CHANCE THAT HE KNOWS HOW TO BE HOME AND NOT BE HOME, AND I WOULDN'T KNOW HOW HE WAS DOING IT.

THANK YOU.

HERO FIGHTING HERO. HERO FIGHTING HERO.

I WONDER WHAT THE *CRIMINALS* ARE DOING.

YES, THANK YOU.

TONY?

I WANT TO GET MY KID OUT OF HERE.

YEAH, NO $%#@.

WAIT.

WE'RE DONE HERE.

HEAD ON BACK TO THE TOWER.

WHAT ARE *YOU* GOING TO DO?

I'LL BE RIGHT BEHIND YOU.

OKAY...

JUST WEEKS BEFORE THE CIVIL WAR WENT FULL-SCALE--

--WE ALL FIRST HOOKED UP AS AVENGERS BECAUSE WE WERE TRYING TO STOP A PRISON BREAK.

BECAUSE SOMEONE LET ALL THE CRIMINALS OUT OF THEIR CAGES. NOT SOME...ALL OF THEM.

AND WHEN WE WENT CHASING AFTER THEM, WE FOUND OUT THAT--

I KNOW THIS--WE--

YOU NEED TO HEAR IT AGAIN.

WE WENT OFF TO THE SAVAGE LAND AND WHAT DID WE FIND? WE FOUND OUT THAT THERE WAS SOMETHIN' REALLY ROTTEN IN S.H.I.E.L.D.

THEN WE FOUND OUT THERE WAS SOMETHING ROTTEN IN HYDRA TOO...

AND ALL OF A SUDDEN, NICK FURY WENT BYE-BYE.

AND ALL OF A SUDDEN, THE GOVERNMENT TURNS US ON EACH OTHER.

AND ALL OF A SUDDEN IT ALL WENT BACKWARDS ON US REAL FAST.

AND I'M NOT JUST STEAMIN' BECAUSE WE LOST THE WAR AND CAP'S DEAD.

NO, I'M STEAMIN' BECAUSE I THINK THERE'S A LOT MORE GOIN' ON HERE. I FEEL MANIPULATED. I FEEL SOMEONE PULLING MY STRINGS.

S.H.I.E.L.D., HYDRA, OUR SECRET WAR, THE CIVIL WAR....

I THINK THEY'RE CONNECTED.

DO YOU?

AND DOES THAT IDEA SCARE THE HOLY CRAP OUT OF YOU?

IF IT DOESN'T AND Y'WANNA GO? GO.

GO BACK TO YOUR PAL, TONY.

I'M ASKING-- AS A GROUP-- WHAT ARE WE GOING TO DO?

WHO IS THAT?

IT'S ANOTHER DAMN TRICK.

WHO IS IT?

OH, MAN...

IT'S CLINT BARTON.

YOU KNEW HIM AS HAWKEYE.

I THOUGHT HE WAS DEAD.

HE'S.

≈WHEW≈ BECAUSE IF HE'S DEAD AND I CAN SEE HIM...

...THAT'S NOT GOOD FOR ME.

IT'S A TRICK.

HE CAME TO ME MONTHS BACK, BEFORE THE WAR AND ALL OF THIS, LOOKING FOR WANDA MAXIMOFF.

I TOLD HIM I DIDN'T KNOW WHERE SHE WAS AND GAVE HIM SOME COUNSEL AS HE TRIES TO MAKE HIS WAY BACK INTO THE WORLD.

HE HAD NO INTEREST IN HIS OLD LIFE. I THINK WE CAN TRUST HIM.

YEAH? LET'S SAY HI.

YOU'RE ONE OF THE OLD-SCHOOL AVENGERS, HAWKEYE, WHY AREN'T YOU WITH THEM?

WITH TONY STARK AND HIS CORPORATE PUPPET MUPPET BABIES?

YEAH? NO.

NO, I JUST CAME BACK HERE TO TELL DOC STRANGE THAT I'M OKAY.

I OWED HIM THAT.

YOU'LL HAVE TO EXCUSE US FOR THINKING THIS IS ALL JUST A BIG PILE OF HORSE--

WELL, THAT'S FINE.

YOU ALL GO BACK TO WHATEVER IT WAS YOU WERE DOING AND I'LL BE ON MY WAY.

NO. NO, YOU CAN STAY.

NAH, IT'S OKAY.

DOC, THANKS FOR EVERYTHING. I MEAN IT.

WHAT ARE YOU GOING TO DO?

WELL, NOW THAT I FINALLY FOUND A WAY BACK INTO THIS COUNTRY, I'M GOING TO DO WHATEVER THE HELL I CAN TO HONOR CAPTAIN AMERICA'S WORLD-VIEW.

THE GUY MEANT EVERYTHING TO ME, AND IF I WAS HERE TO *STOP* THE WAR, I WOULD HAVE.

WITH A *BULLET* IF I HAD TO.

YEAH, WELL, WE WERE CAP'S TEAM, Y'KNOW.

YEAH?

AND WHAT ARE YOU DOING ABOUT IT?

WHY AREN'T YOU STORMING THAT AVENGERS "TOWER" AND SHOVING THE SUPERHUMAN REGISTRATION ACT UP TONY STARK'S @#$?

WE'RE DOING THAT ON SATURDAY.

TONIGHT WE'RE GOING TO JAPAN.

NOT WITH HIM.

NO?

GUY COMES BACK FROM THE DEAD RIGHT AFTER WE--

WHAT'S IN JAPAN?

SOMETHING CAP WANTED--

NO. STOP. STOP IT.

LET HIM GO.

LUKE...

LUKE...

GO BACK TO YOUR PAL TONY. AND YOU TELL HIM FROM ME THAT THERE ISN'T--

LUKE. IT REALLY IS HIM AND HE REALLY IS--

I CAN BARELY TRUST THE PEOPLE IN THIS ROOM. NOW I GOT CASPER THE FRIENDLY GHOST--

DON'T PULL A HAMMY, CAGE--I'LL LEAVE.

WE COULD USE HIM.

WE COULD.

WAS IT JUST ME WHO WAS AN HOUR AGO TRICKED BY FORMER FRIENDS INTO ALMOST--?

WOULD IT MAKE YOU FEEL BETTER IF I CAST THE SPELL OF TARTASHI ON US?

WELL...?

THAT'S IT.

WHAT'S IT?

EVERYONE HERE IS PURE OF INTENTION.

HOW DO YOU *KNOW?*

BECAUSE IF YOU WEREN'T, YOU WOULD BE HAVING A SEIZURE RIGHT NOW.

WELL, THAT'S NICE.

SHE LAUGHED. SHE'S NEVER LAUGHED BEFORE.

A BABY-- THERE'S NOTHING MORE PURE OF SPIRIT.

SERIOUSLY, WHAT'S IN JAPAN?

A FRIEND WHO NEEDS HELP.

CAP SENT HER INTO THE FIELD AND NOW SHE'S IN TROUBLE.

ALL RIGHT, YEAH, OKAY...

GET YOUR HAWKEYE ON AND COME WITH.

I'M NOT HAWKEYE ANYMORE.

TSK. SORRY, IT'S COSTUMES ONLY.

WHAT?

LIKE A NINJA?

JAPAN, NOW.

YOU *AIN'T* GONNA WIN THIS FIGHT, ELEKTRA.

NOT THE BEST WAY TO START YOUR REIGN AS QUEEN OF THE JAPANESE UNDERWORLD.

BUT ON THE OTHER HAND, NO PUN INTENDED... YOU *NEED* US.

YOU READ THE PAPER--WE'RE CRIMINALS NOW. THAT'S HOW IT IS NOW.

SO CRIMINAL TO CRIMINAL... LET'S TALK.

WHAT ARE YOU ON ABOUT?

WE HAVE NOTHING TO FIGHT OVER, YOU GUYS AND US.

WE *DON'T?*

WE DON'T!

(WOW, I COMPLETELY MISREAD THE ROOM.)

YOU'LL LIVE WITHOUT HER. IT'S NOT WORTH THE FIGHT.

IT'S JUST BAD BUSINESS.

YOU REALLY THINK SHE'S *WORTH* HOWEVER MANY MEN YOU'LL LOSE IF YOU COME AT US LIKE THIS?

I DON'T KNOW EVERYTHING ABOUT THE HAND, BUT AT SOME POINT, YOU *GOTTA* RUN OUT OF DUDES IN ROBES, RIGHT?

MEANWHILE, WE HAVE LARGER ITEMS ON THE AGENDA.

DO YOU KNOW WHY?

DO I KNOW WHY *WHAT?*

DO YOU KNOW WHY EVERYTHING IS UPSIDE DOWN?

CAGE... WHAT ARE YOU DOING?

NO, WE'RE GOING TO SETTLE THIS LIKE--

WE'RE NOT TRYING TO TAKE ANYTHING FROM YOU THAT WASN'T OURS, ELEKTRA.

WE DON'T *WANT* YOUR TERRITORY. WE'RE NOT TRYING TO *STOP* YOU FROM DOING WHAT YOU'RE DOING HERE.

WE'RE GOING HOME TO AMERICA AND WE'RE TAKING MAYA LOPEZ WITH US.

WE *WANT* MAYA LOPEZ.

AGENDA?

WHAT AGENDA?

S.H.I.E.L.D., THE SUPERHUMAN CIVIL WAR, HYDRA FALLING APART AROUND YOU...

...AND NOW, ALL OF A SUDDEN, *YOU'RE* RUNNING THE JAPANESE UNDERWORLD.

EVERYTHING IS BACKWARDS, UPSIDE DOWN, TOPSY-TURVY...

WHY?

TALKIN' IT OUT.

NO, YOU'RE NOT. YOU'RE LETTING HER WIN.

CHK

WELL! *I'M* FIGHTING NINJAS AGAIN, EVEN THOUGH I *SPECIFICALLY* SAID I'M DONE FIGHTING NINJAS.

WELCOME TO YOUR NEW LIFE, MAYA LOPEZ...

GGGKK...

**NEW AVENGERS #27 & MIGHTY AVENGERS #1 COMBINED VARIANTS BY LEINIL YU**

**NEW AVENGERS #27 RETAILER VARIANT
BY LEINIL YU**

**NEW AVENGERS #31 SKETCH VARIANT
BY LEINIL YU**

#31

GIRL, YOU CAN'T BURN ME! YOU CAN'T CUT ME! SO STOP TRYIN'!

I'M GOING TO TAKE YOUR EYES.

=SNIFF=

THE
HELL IS
THAT?

ここからの退去!
今、皆!

ここからの退去!

HEY, ARE YOU GUYS TALKING ABOUT *ME*, BECAUSE THAT'S JUST--HEY!

ARE YOU *KIDDING* ME?

THAT'S *IT*?

ZZATGCT

OH, NO! DON'T YOU EVEN--

WHAT? WHY DID THEY DO *THAT*? WHAT *IS* IT?

COME ON...

(GOOD, EVERYONE'S STILL ALIVE.)

SAY WHAT YOU WILL ABOUT THE HAND-- THEY EITHER RUN AWAY OR DISAPPEAR WITH A POOF OF STINKY SMOKE.

THEY NEVER LEAVE...

...A...   ...BODY...